SECRETS OF
REDDING GLEN

REDDING GLEN

The Natural History of a Wooded Valley

JO POLSENO

GOLDEN PRESS · NEW YORK

WESTERN PUBLISHING COMPANY, INC.
RACINE, WISCONSIN

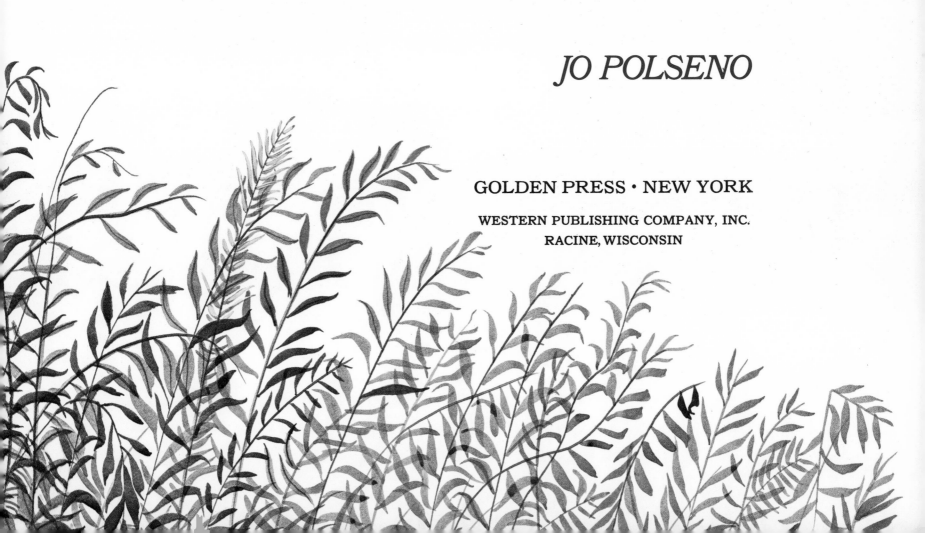

In Redding there is a glen where the wild geese fly and
the salamanders live…where the owl hoots in the moonlight
and the wood thrush sings in the day. Wild grapes cling
to the beech tree and the loon cries out in the night.
The hills that surround the cove give sanctuary to the
fox and the deer. The silence of a deep-shadowed summer's
day is broken only by the drone of a cicada or the silver
song of a scarlet tanager.

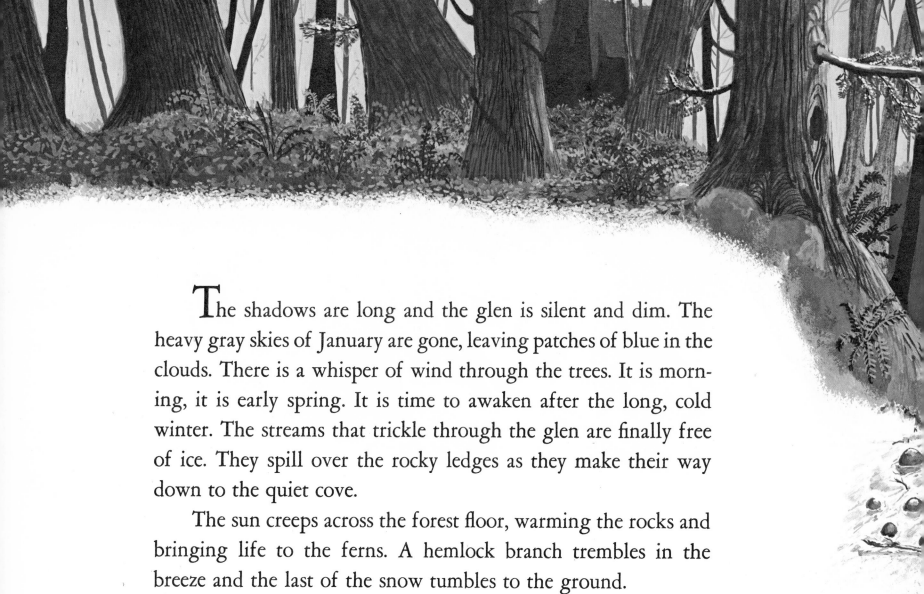

The shadows are long and the glen is silent and dim. The heavy gray skies of January are gone, leaving patches of blue in the clouds. There is a whisper of wind through the trees. It is morning, it is early spring. It is time to awaken after the long, cold winter. The streams that trickle through the glen are finally free of ice. They spill over the rocky ledges as they make their way down to the quiet cove.

The sun creeps across the forest floor, warming the rocks and bringing life to the ferns. A hemlock branch trembles in the breeze and the last of the snow tumbles to the ground.

...Redding Glen is awake.

A spring peeper strikes a single note to signal the coming of March. The melting snow has created pockets of amber-colored pools in which the tiny frogs will lay their milky-white eggs. The peeper strikes another note, this time a little louder, a little more insistent. He is answered by a second peeper, then another, then still another. The chorus swells to a crescendo as the glen rings out with its first spring concert while a touch of winter is still in the air.

Purple trilliums appear by the edge of the pool and Christmas ferns lift their fiddleheads a little higher each day. The peepers will sing until late April, then vanish for the rest of the year.

13

A ring of mist circles the moon. Will it rain in three days or will it snow? The days pass and the nights grow warmer. Gray, windy March turns into April green and the rings around the moon turn into April showers. Each day the woods are filled with new sounds and new songs as more birds arrive from the South. The peepers still sing at night, but now they are joined by the booming voice of the great horned owl and the lonely call of the whippoorwill.

Marsh marigolds and dogtooth violets bloom on the banks of the streams and the first handful of watercress is ready to be gathered. The trilliums are fading and the milkweed is waiting for June. The earth is no longer cold and hard; there is the sweet smell of ferns in the air.

15

16

Down by the edge of the pond where the skunk cabbage grows and the arrowheads nod, a green heron perches on a fallen branch, waiting patiently for a fish or a frog to swim by. His long beak is as sharp as a spear and just as deadly. He stands motionless for perhaps fifteen minutes, a seemingly lifeless form. Then, with a rapier-swift thrust of his beak, he spears an unsuspecting fish.

Nearby, at the water's edge, the quiet of the forest is broken by a large, dead limb that crashes into the pond. With a loud *skeee-ow!* the startled green heron takes to the sky. A spotted turtle climbs the half-sunken branch and basks in the warmth of the sun.

The morning sun burns the mist from the cove. A Canada goose, swimming in a circle around a small island of grass, lowers his head and hisses. He is protecting his mate who is sitting on four white eggs. A muskrat, who might destroy the nest, hears the angry goose and quickly swims away.

In a few weeks the fuzzy yellow goslings will hatch. They will follow their parents wherever they go and will hide under the adults' wings when they are frightened.

The sun climbs higher in the sky. The mist is gone. From the marsh grass on the island comes the sound of the two geese softly honking.

19

A loud, shattering rattle comes from the sky as the belted kingfisher announces his arrival from the South. He is the true king of fishermen. With wings held close to his body, the kingfisher dives straight into the water. Emerging soaking wet with a fish in his mouth, he flies to the nearest branch to dry his feathers. Many times during the day, you will hear his distinctive rattle as this expert fisherman searches the river for a fish swimming close to the surface.

Somewhere along the bank of the river the kingfisher will dig a hole with his powerful beak and build a nest for his mate. Soon there will be as many as eight little kingfishers, imitating their parents and learning how to dive.

21

When the barn swallows return to the bridge by the glen, spring is here to stay. These swift and graceful swallows dip and dive, skimming the surface of the water while catching mayflies on the wing.

From morning to dusk, from May to September, the air will be filled with the *whirr* of their shiny blue wings and flashes of their chestnut-colored bellies. The swallows have come back to the glen to build their nests of mud and straw beneath the eaves of the bridge. Evenings, when the wind dies down and the water is as smooth as glass, the swallows gather by the bridge where they will roost for the night. They chirp, twitter, and scold until their voices are hushed by the dark.

24

The forest is still and the night is dark. There is a rustle in the reeds by the water's edge . . . a grunt, a growl, and a splash. A fat, furry animal with bright, beady eyes has just caught a slippery green frog. That sly-looking face and that sad-looking frog belong to the crafty raccoon.

The raccoon is a skilled hunter of crayfish and frogs and cannot resist an ear of sweet corn. In fact, he will eat almost anything. He enjoys rummaging through garbage cans looking for lumps of sugar and half-eaten sandwiches. He has a weakness for fresh-laid eggs and every once in a while gets caught in someone's chicken coop. There's no other way to put it—the raccoon is an amusing thief who rarely, if ever, gets caught.

Three days of summer rain have fallen on the glen. Quiet brooks that once flowed gently down to the channel have turned into raging streams. The muddy water crashes over rocks and boulders, creating foamy waterfalls as it plunges down the hill. Ferns and flowers have been beaten flat by the deluge and dead limbs litter the forest floor.

Mushrooms of all sizes and colors have sprung from the wet earth. A spotted salamander crawls over the moist ground looking for a new place to hide. In the cove, fish feast on the worms and insects washed down from the slopes. The rains end. The sun slowly appears, bringing with it the smell of cinnamon ferns, pine trees, and the warm, wet earth.

The strangest sound that comes from the glen is the voice of the loon that laughs in the night. From across the pond you might see him before he suddenly disappears beneath the surface of the water, where this powerful, deep-diving bird can swim as fast as a fish.

On quiet nights in August, when the water is smooth and calm, you can hear his lonely laughter as he calls out from the dark. The loon will stay in the glen until the pond freezes over. Then he will often fly north instead of south, to spend a cold and stormy winter along the North Atlantic coast.

It is evening, and the wood thrush sings his twilight song. In the fading light a bat flits over the surface of the quiet water. A nighthawk plunges from the sky, opens his large mouth, and captures an insect. From an old tree stump the bright eyes of a white-footed mouse peer watchfully. He looks nervously about, then scurries for an acorn half-hidden by the fallen leaves.

The forest is nearly dark as the moon rises from behind the hills. Somewhere in the night there drifts the song of an oven-bird. The mouse peers out of his hole again and gathers more food by the light of the moon.

There is a burst of feathers in the air and the blurred image of a large brown bird disappears through the tangled branches of the underbrush. It is the ruffed grouse. Until this elusive bird explodes at one's feet he is almost impossible to find, for he blends perfectly with the leaves on the ground.

Early some morning you might hear a strange drumming sound echoing throughout the forest. It is the male ruffed grouse beating his wings rapidly to his sides. The sound can be heard for great distances. It is the grouse's way of claiming his nesting territory—and let all other birds beware.

33

Tiny specks in the sky circle and float gently toward the earth. They become larger and larger. Now they look like strips of black paper being blown about by the wind. Suddenly they take the shape of large black birds almost the size of eagles. These are turkey vultures riding the wind currents that rise above the hills.

Summer skies in Redding, with vultures making lazy circles in the clouds . . . the birds rise and fall with the wind, barely moving their wings. Not far from the glen they roost in a tall, dead tree that juts from the base of a craggy ledge. At dawn, the morning breeze will sweep them back to the sky where they will soar for the rest of the day.

There is a disturbing swirl in the quiet brown waters of the cove. A large, fierce-looking pickerel with powerful jaws and sharp teeth is in pursuit of a sunfish. The tiny fish leaps out of the water, then plunges deep to hide in the weeds that twist and wave at the bottom of the pond. The frightened sunfish remains motionless in the weeds until the pickerel swims away.

The pickerel is a savage hunter who preys on other fish. All the creatures in the pond fear him and flee for their lives when he is near. Occasionally, he will even capture a stray duckling or a young bird that has fallen from its nest.

The shadow of a fish hawk passes over the cove. This time it is the pickerel who heads for the weeds.

A strange and solitary bird lives in the glen, a bird seldom seen and rarely heard. It is the woodcock, who hunts in the mud flats in the dark of the night. He uses his long bill to probe in the mud, searching for nightcrawlers and other worms. This secretive bird comes to the cove each evening and is gone before the sun rises.

Somewhere in the forest there is a secret place where the woodcock nests, a place that nobody knows. Listen, some night, for the rustle of his wings down in the mud flats by the edge of the cove.

Midsummer, and the wild grapes are plump and bright green. A summer silence settles upon the glen. The birds no longer sing as they did in the spring, for the mating season is past and they are busy rearing their young. There is an abrupt flash of wings as a plain-looking gray bird alights among the grape leaves. The catbird samples a grape to see if it is ripe.

This inconspicuous bird can imitate a variety of sounds. He can meow like a cat, squawk like a chicken, even squeak like

40

a rusty old gate. On many a moonlit night, when the woods are silent and a blanket of mist hangs over the glen, a sudden burst of song rings out. It is the catbird singing his solo until the moon dips behind the face of a cloud.

A large blue-gray bird descends from the darkening sky. Gracefully extending his long, slender legs, the great blue heron lands gently in the reeds. Although this large bird does not nest in the glen, he comes each evening to the inlet to feed on fish and frogs.

The heron is a solitary hunter. Standing in the shallow end of the cove, not moving a single feather, he looks like a statue frozen in time. Suddenly there is a lightning-swift *sa-wish!* His sharp beak disappears into the water and comes up with a fish.

Beginning at dusk and continuing until dawn, a mysterious barking sound echoes throughout the woods. Wild dogs, young foxes—what can the sound be? Four bright yellow eyes peer out of the dark. They are the eyes of two young great horned owls, and they are crying out for food. Although they are almost full grown, they cannot yet take care of themselves, so they wait impatiently for their parent to return with her night's catch. The pine bough trembles as the mother alights with a dead skunk in her talons and the owlets begin to feed.

Soon the parents will return to the roosting tree less and less often. Before the summer is over the downy owls will spread their huge wings, leap into the night, and learn to hunt in the dark for themselves.

On the far side of the cove the reeds hang heavy after a morning rain. The level of the water has risen and now covers the grassy glade where the heron hunts. A morning mist rises, like smoke, from the pond. Two small wood ducks who have spent the summer in the glen swim out from behind a clump of marsh grass. A half-dozen ducklings will soon follow. They are waiting to hear a soft, raspy whistle from the mother duck signaling that there is nothing to fear.

The wood duck nests in hollow trees, sometimes at quite a distance from water. When newly hatched, the young have very

sharp toenails that enable them to climb out of the deep, dark tree cavity. Sometimes as many as twelve ducklings tumble out of a dead tree trunk, land softly on the leaves, and follow their parents to the water.

The swift and ruthless Cooper's hawk, also known as the big blue darter and the chicken hawk, is the most feared creature in the glen. The explosive ruffed grouse is no match for this dread bird of prey, nor is the alert blue jay safe from his claws. He will plunge into a prickly brier patch in pursuit of a young grouse and chase him on foot if necessary.

The Cooper's hawk is a hunter of the deep forests. With his short wings and long tail, he is able to fly through the tangled thickets of the woods with great speed and accuracy. Birds do not sing and the forest is silent when the big blue darter appears in the glen.

The first frost has come to the glen. Day by day the leaves of the sycamore tree have been falling to the ground. Crickets and katydids chirp in the hazy afternoon. Chipmunks are busy filling their burrows with nuts that must last through the long, cold winter. Soon the autumn winds will blow the remaining leaves to the ground. But today, the sun rises above the mist and the afternoon promises to be hot. The smell of wild grapes, like wine, fills the air as the insects drone on through the last few days of October's warmth.

52

A yearling pokes his head between the dried leaves of a beech tree. He cautiously approaches the still, dark waters of the cove. The trees are almost bare and the young deer must be careful when he comes to the cove to drink. Later, when deep snows carpet the glen, he will stay in the high, rocky hills, where the hemlock trees grow thick and where there are many places for him to hide. If the winter is mild, perhaps he will find an abandoned apple orchard and feed on the frozen brown fruit.

The young deer twitches his tail nervously and takes a few more cautious steps. From the reeds comes the raspy whistle of a wood duck. All is quiet, all is safe. The yearling lowers his head and drinks.

Cattails and reeds are alive as red-winged blackbirds arrive and fill the air with their *chekks* and chirpings. The first of the large flocks is gathering for its long flight southward. Each day, more and more birds drop from the sky to join the enormous flock. Soon they will rise, like a huge black cloud, and follow the hills and valleys to where the winter sun is warm.

A strong wind has come down from the ridge. Tall, thin reeds make a dry, slapping sound. The birds become excited, fluttering and rising in small groups. In a moment the sky will be filled with hundreds of wings as the birds are carried away by the wind.

Throughout the day large flocks of birds have been passing over the glen. Hundreds of swallows have gathered at the bridge, and new swarms of blackbirds arrive. Mallards and black ducks quack nervously in the cove. When the glen freezes over they will fly to the open coastal waters.

A small flock of Canada geese splashes down on the pond. Their loud honking adds to the noise and the excitement. In the morning, a large old female will take to the air. She will be followed by the rest of the geese. One by one they will fall behind her in their well-known V-formation and she will lead them to the warm waters of the South.

57

The somber gray tones of November have fallen upon the forest. The marsh grass has turned a brittle brown and there is a thin sheet of ice on the pond. Autumn leaves lie frozen in the water where they fell. A solitary blackbird calls from the reeds, but there is no answer.

Soon there will be only winter sounds in the glen. Chick-adees and titmice will call from the hemlock trees while tiny winter wrens flit through the brambles and briers. Blue Jays will shatter the silence with their harsh voices as they make their daily patrol. There is a stillness in the glen as the first snowflakes softly begin to fall.

60

During the night snow has fallen silently on the glen. Hemlock boughs bend with its weight. The sounds of the forest are sharp and clear in the cold winter air. A flock of crows has discovered a sleeping barred owl and they will give him no rest until he flies away. Somewhere in the hills a yearling paws at the frozen ground, looking for tender moss. The trail of a fox circles the pond, then disappears into the pines.

From across the cove comes a new sound, a good sound. It is the hushed voices of two young boys who have just discovered Redding Glen.